Gary Shapiro
and Azak

Gary Shapiro credits Dr. Paul Chaffee, director, with allowing him access to Azak to study cognitive abilities in orangutans for his Master's thesis. He sat with her every day for 22 months and produced some valuable information. As a result, Gary has gone on to international work with Orangutans and has his own organization called Orang Utan Republik Education Initiative dedicated to saving wild orangutans from extinction through education. Information can be found on his website: www.orangutanrepublik.org.

Azak spent a happy two years in the new exhibit with companions, grass, and swings. She often exhibited her intelligence in the new exhibit with her problem solving abilities.
She died March 20, 2003 and her loss was deeply felt.

In Recognition:

To the Zoo Staff who generously
shared their stories with me.

A special thanks to

Mary Swanson for her photos and stories.
And to my editor and friend Marcia Dobbs.

This book is dedicated to
Dr Paul Chaffee
my inspiration
and true love.

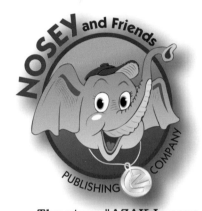

The story "AZAK Learns to Read" is an imprint of Nosey and Friends Publishing Co.
Published by Nosey and Friends Publishing Co.
5647 N. Prospect
Fresno, CA 93711
Copyright © 2005 Jean Chaffee
Fresno, California
All rights reserved.
Printed in South Korea
(Second Printing)
10 9 8 7 6 5 4 3 2 1

Library of Congress Control Number: 2005907981
Jean Chaffee
The story of "AZAK Learns to Read" / written by Jean Chaffee
Illustrated by Ernie "Hergie" Hergenroeder
Summary: The story of Azak the Orangutan learning to read actually happened during
Gary Shapiro's quest to earn his Masters Thesis in cognitive abilities with Orangutans.
ISBN: 0-9748075-2-4 (Hardcover)
Copyright to include all characters, design & story concept.

AZAK

Learns to Read

by
Jean Chaffee

Illustrated by:
Ernie Hergenroeder
"HERGIE"

TRUE ZOO TO
YOU STORIES

Suma and Sumac lived in the zoo and already had 3 babies: Rosie, Roger and Denny. One morning a large group of visiting zookeepers was at the zoo and they stopped to watch the beautiful orangutans.

1

Suddenly someone spotted tiny eyes peeking out behind Suma's arm.
"Look!" they said, "she is holding a new baby! "
"Ohhh! How cute!" all the zookeepers said.

Her mother held her close to keep her safe and warm.
Suma and Sumac loved their new baby who was given the name, AZAK, which stands for the **A**ssociation of **Z**oo **K**eepers.

Doc Chaffee, the zoo director, was so proud he puffed up his chest and popped his buttons.

Pop! Pop! Pop!

Sumac sat patiently while Azak climbed on him like a jungle gym.
She pulled her father's long, orange hair.
Sometimes she played hide-and-seek underneath his long coat.

"Peek-A Boo, Azak!"

When Azak was two years old, she moved into the nursery where she met a young chimpanzee named Brucie. At first Azak was very shy, so the nursery aide carried the two of them everywhere until they became good friends.

Visitors flocked to the zoo to catch a peek of the two apes in the nursery window.

"I see Azak!" *said one.*
"I see Brucie!" *shouted another.*

Azak and Brucie blew kisses and made funny faces at the people and everyone laughed.

Azak and Brucie had lots of fun.
They ran and played.
They screamed and laughed.
They ate and slept
together all day.

Whoop!
Whoop!
Whoop!

Azak was very happy.

8

In the morning, she ate cereal and bananas.
Afterward, she washed and rinsed her dishes.
The nursery aides played games with Azak.
She played with blocks and loved to finger paint.
The zoo even sold some
of her paintings.

9

Azak watched everything the zookeepers did. One day, a zookeeper gave her a key and Azak figured out how to open her cage door. Then she ran down the hallway to Doc's office and jumped into his lap.

"Are you going to help me run the zoo?" asked Doc.

10

One morning Doc told Azak,
"Today you are going to school.
We want to find out how smart
you really are".
Azak was all excited about
going to school.

Mr. Gary was Azak's teacher.
He brought her a box of plastic letters.
"Is this something good to eat?"
she thought as she chewed on them.

Yuck!

She spit the letters
across the floor.

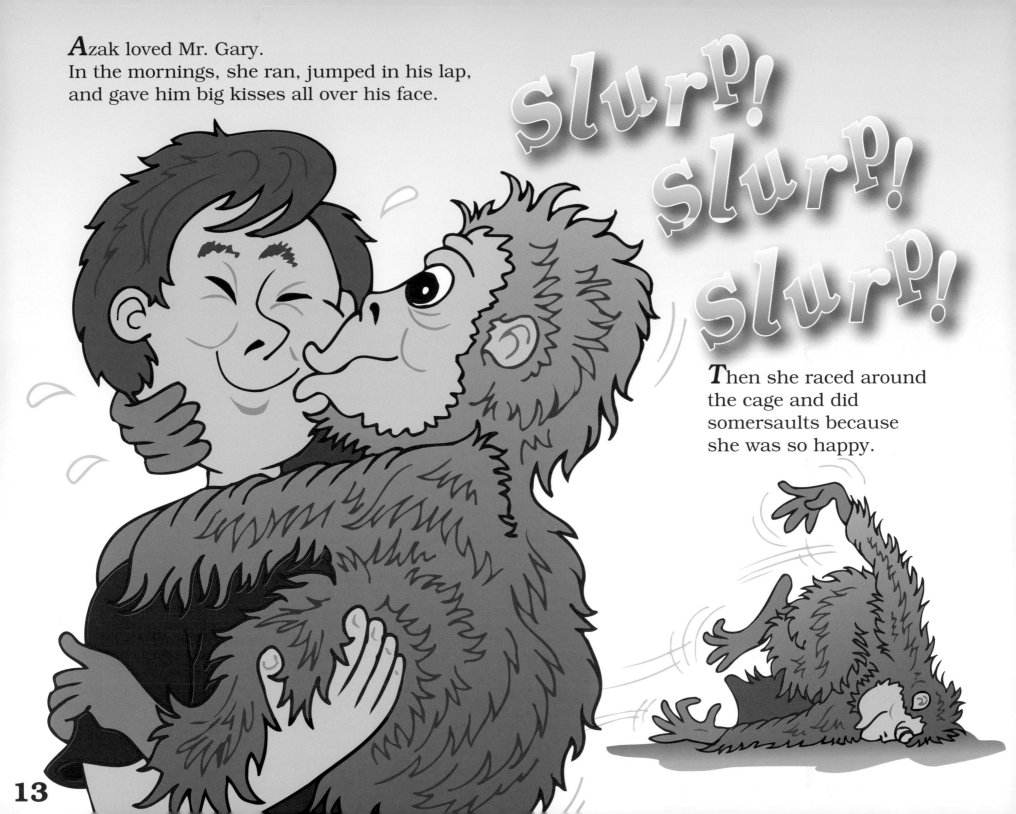

*A*zak loved Mr. Gary.
In the mornings, she ran, jumped in his lap,
and gave him big kisses all over his face.

Slurp!
Slurp!
Slurp!

*T*hen she raced around
the cage and did
somersaults because
she was so happy.

13

The teacher put a purple "X" on the board.
"Azak, this "X" is your name."

Mr. Gary rewarded Azak
with a hug and a treat when
she found her name.
*"Oh, Azak. You
are so smart!"*

14

Every day Azak and Mr. Gary sat and played with the letters.
She learned her colors, capital letters, and lower case letters.
A red "G" was for Gary. A yellow lower case "h" meant spoon,
but a capital blue "H" meant brush.

Playing a game like Scrabble, Azak learned to put the letters in the right order to make a sentence.

"Gary brush Azak," she wrote.

When Mr. Gary smiled, she ran to get the brush and sat very still while he brushed her hair.

16

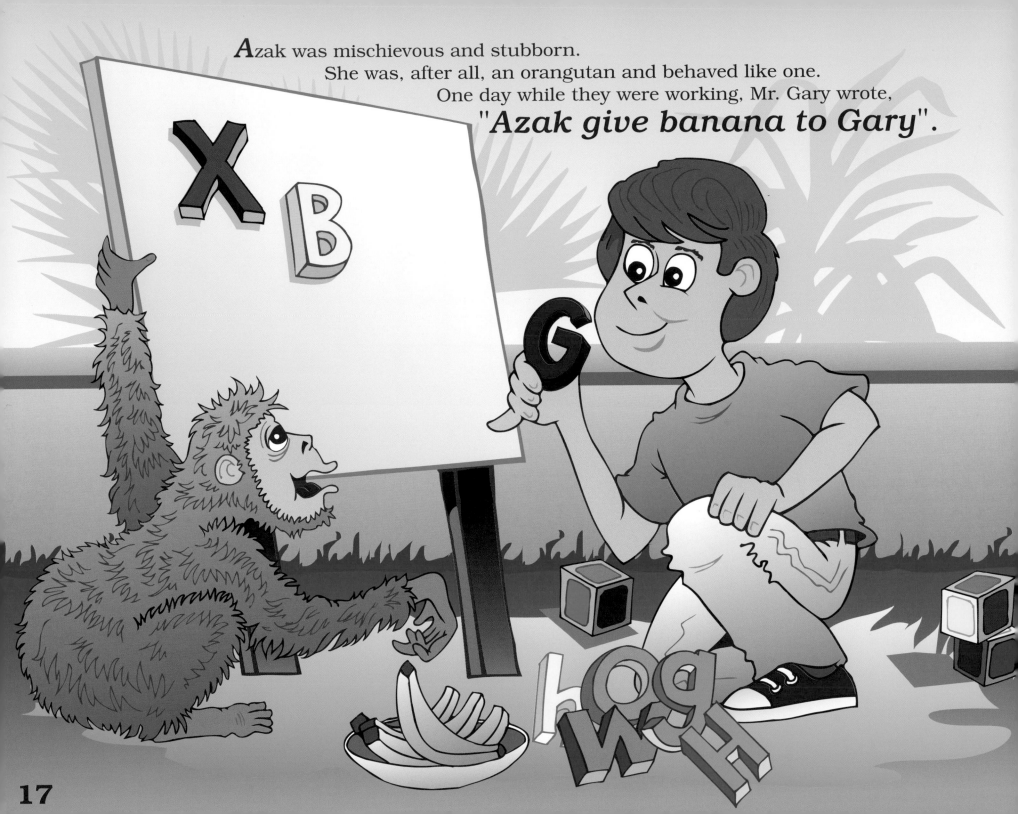

Azak was mischievous and stubborn.
She was, after all, an orangutan and behaved like one.
One day while they were working, Mr. Gary wrote,
"Azak give banana to Gary".

Aazk picked up her banana and very slowly held it out.
"Good girl, Azak!
Thank you for the banana,"
Mr. Gary said as he took Azak's banana from her hand."

18

Mr. Gary gave Azak a cup of water for giving him the treat. Azak took a sip and then threw the cup across the floor.

Crash! Smash! Bang!

She waited a minute then ran to get the cup and leaped into Gary's lap for a big hug.

19

One day Mr. Gary tested her. He brought her some orange juice. She wanted it, but did not know a letter for orange juice. He waited and waited while Azak thought and thought.

20

She sat for a long time looking at the orange juice and her letters. She picked up her letters one by one and tried them on the board. "No, this isn't right", she thought.

Finally, she held up the letter "**O**" for orange and the letter "**W**" for water and put them together.
She looked at Mr. Gary with a little smile.

22

1969 - 2003

Azak lived her entire life at Chaffee Zoo

24

Be sure to collect all of these other delightful true zoo animal stories by Jean Chaffee and complete your set.